THE
TAROT JOURNAL

THE TAROT JOURNAL

*Record your readings and gain
insight into your life*

MELISSA TURNBERRY

ARCTURUS

ARCTURUS

This edition published in 2021 by Arcturus Publishing Limited
26/27 Bickels Yard, 151–153 Bermondsey Street,
London SE1 3HA

ISBN: 978-1-3988-1421-9
AD010233UK

Printed in China

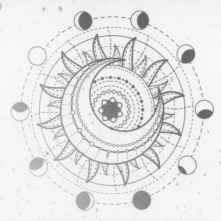

INTRODUCTION

This journal is the perfect companion for anyone who has begun to do their own tarot readings and wants to make notes about either the readings themselves or the thoughts that they may evoke.

The tarot unlocks in the psyche messages from a vast mysterious universe, one that may be psychologically located in one's own subconscious. Modern tarot readers are as likely to advise you on how to approach forthcoming challenges as they are to prophesize about what is due to happen to you. The tarot's universal symbols speak of a journey – our personal path through life – and there is much to recommend them as a guide to discovering what concerns lie just under the surface of your consciousness.

When you do a reading, remember that your fate is not predetermined and outcomes will change as you change your attitude, behaviour and responses. A reading is a snapshot of what is coming in the next 6–12 months for you and it is rare that you will be able to draw cards accurately for any longer period of time than that.

As a helpful reminder, this journal contains a section at the beginning in which the meaning behind each of the tarot cards is explained, but which spread pattern you select is your decision. Every time you do a reading, record it in these pages, along with the time and date, so you can explore how your readings change over time as you confront the changing aspects of life that they have revealed.

THE FOOL

KEYWORDS:
fresh start, beginning, freedom, courage, openness, trust, risk-taking

The Fool is shown standing on the edge of a precipice, bag and rose in hand, with a dog at his heels. He is stepping into the unknown, alone except for his trusty dog, full of expectation and potential and unfettered by the doubts and cynicism that come with experience. The card suggests a choice must be made and a journey started into unknown territory. Courage is required to take the first step. The Fool is unaware of, and unprepared for, what awaits him, but through new experiences he will discover his true potential.

THE MAGICIAN

KEYWORDS:
skills, potential, mastery, resourcefulness, will, power, creativity, action

The Magician stands next to a table upon which lie all the implements of his trade. These represent the four tarot suits and the four elements. Wand in hand, the Magician is about to use his powers to command his will. On his head his hat is almost like the infinity symbol (explicitly shown in some decks), known as the cosmic lemniscate, which represents the eternal and immortal force of energy. At this first stage of his journey, the Fool realizes that he has all the resources he needs to gain mastery over the material world of opposites and duality. He has become the Magician, an authority figure who has the power to do good. Creativity and resourcefulness are needed to overcome obstacles.

THE HIGH PRIESTESS

KEYWORDS:
wisdom, intuition, mystery, secrets, hidden knowledge, unseen influences at work

The High Priestess is also described as the veiled Isis. In the Rider-Waite-Smith deck, she is seated between two pillars which represent the great universal principles and mark the entrance to the sacred temple. She holds a book containing esoteric knowledge on her lap. She stands for hidden knowledge, wisdom and intuition. When she appears in a spread, it could indicate that some hidden forces are at work in a situation and one must look inwards for the answer. Trust in your own resources and ensure that your view aligns with what others suggest before you follow any external advice. The High Priestess represents the feminine principle incorporating the cycles of life and the creative force of the female.

THE EMPRESS

KEYWORDS:
abundance, pleasure, contentment, creativity, nature, nurture, balance, fullness, fertility, renewal

The Empress is Isis unveiled. Seated on her throne, she radiates the beauty that comes from harmony with nature. She is the Earth Mother, in charge of the seasons, the fertility of the soil and production of our food. At this stage of the journey, the Fool realizes that he needs to look after his health and physical needs.

The Empress indicates the possibility of marriage and motherhood as well as material gain. With careful attention and nurturing, a creative project will bear fruit. A situation is full of promise and has great potential to turn out as desired. It is usually a good omen to find her in a reading where the querent has a desire to manifest a good relationship.

THE
EMPEROR

THE
HIEROPHANT

KEYWORDS:
judgement, decision, action,
responsibility, challenge,
effectiveness, satisfaction from
achievement

KEYWORDS:
law, tradition, religion,
meaning, philosophy, teaching,
learning, vision

The Emperor is the card of fathering and indicates focus and the energy of accomplishment. The Emperor challenges the Fool to build something lasting to be proud of. The Fool is asked to make a decision about what he wants and what he values most in the world. He must then set out to achieve his goal. It will require hard work and unwavering determination and he will be judged on his abilities and the way in which he exercises responsibility. When this card is drawn, someone in a position of authority may offer advice that should be taken seriously and, more importantly, acted upon.

Also called the High Priest or Pope, the Hierophant is a wise teacher, priest or counsellor to whom we may turn at times of personal crisis. Like the High Priestess, the Hierophant is seated between two pillars at the entrance of the temple. However, unlike the High Priestess, the Hierophant represents the outer trappings and traditions of religious practice. At this stage in his journey the Fool must find meaning and seek answers to questions about the purpose of his life. When this card appears in a spread it indicates that we may be searching for meaning and need to approach a situation with a philosophical outlook.

THE LOVERS

THE CHARIOT

KEYWORDS:
love, connection, sexual attraction, union of opposites, new possibilities, temptation, choice

KEYWORDS:
action, control, focus, strength, stability, willpower, conflict, struggle, change, triumph

In the card of the Lovers, we find a man and woman standing next to (and, in some versions, embracing) each other, with the man looking at the woman. The woman is looking up to the sky, where Cupid is watching, and, occasionally, such as in the Marseilles deck here, there is another standing next to them. The card alludes to love, relationship and the family, but the Lovers has also come to represent temptation and the need to make a choice. At this stage of his journey, the Fool finds his match and decides to marry and unite the opposites within. The card suggests that a union is possible and there is hope for a bright future ahead, if temptation can be avoided.

The Chariot card represents gaining control over conflicting forces. The charioteer in the card is trying to control the two horses which are pulling the chariot. The horses – one red, one blue – represent principles pulling in opposite directions. The opposites that were united in the previous Lovers card must now be kept moving in the same direction. At this stage in his journey, the Fool must use all his strength to keep on the right track. By seeing what has to be done and taking control of the situation, obstacles will be overcome. If we manage to keep the opposite forces on the same path, we will go far. Events in the querent's life are moving quickly.

STRENGTH

KEYWORDS:
strength, control, confidence,
balance, integrity, courage,
generosity, compassion

The card of Strength depicts a woman holding open (or forcing closed) the jaws of a lion, apparently without fear of danger. The lion represents our primal urges, the wild and ravenous beast within, yet the woman has succeeded in taming them. Like the Magician, she has an infinity symbol, or cosmic leminiscate, above her head in thes shape of her headwear, indicating that she has achieved a new level of consciousness and understanding. The Fool is gaining mastery over the primal forces that have governed him and his conscious ego is taking control. The card suggests that struggles may be ahead, but we have the courage and confidence to overcome any danger or challenge.

THE HERMIT

KEYWORDS:
solitude, withdrawal, detachment,
caution, patience, prudence,
discretion, limitation

The Hermit stands alone on a mountaintop, holding up a lamp to light his way. He is wearing a cloak and carrying a staff to help him through the tough terrain. He has retreated from society to gain some perspective and look inward for answers. Through patient searching, he gains insight and connects with his intuitive knowledge. The Fool has reached maturity and questions his direction in life. When the Hermit appears in a spread, we may need to retreat from a situation so that we can recharge our batteries and have space to think. We are advised to retreat and work out what is important to us before taking any further action in a matter.

Wheel of Fortune

KEYWORDS:
luck, chance, fortune, destiny,
change, success, new direction

The Wheel of Fortune represents an unexpected element that will change the outcome of a matter. It may be good or bad, but generally indicates a turn of luck for the better and may herald opportunities and a new phase in life. Although we are responsible for shaping our own lives, this card suggests that luck and fortune may come along at any moment and change things for the better. When the Wheel of Fortune is drawn, an unexpected solution to a problem may present itself. Sometimes the card reminds us that 'what goes around comes around', and that past actions will be rewarded.

Justice

KEYWORDS:
fairness, impartiality, balance,
reflection, decision, equality,
truth, correct action

Like the High Priestess and Hierophant, justice is seated between two pillars, suggesting a religious connection. Justice is one of the universal principles upon which society is built. The figure in the card holds a sword and points it upwards, indicating that justice will be upheld. The sword of justice is famously double-edged, however and a balance must be found between two opposing sides for there to be a fair outcome. This is represented by the scales held in her other hand. Following the Wheel of Fortune card, Justice reminds us that we are accountable for our actions and urges us to be honest and fair. This card indicates that justice will eventually prevail.

THE HANGED MAN

KEYWORDS:

patience, waiting, surrender,
sacrifice, wisdom, foresight,
planning, strategy, eventual gain

The card of the Hanged Man depicts a man hanging upside down from a beam. His legs are crossed and he has reached an impasse. No further movement is possible for the time being. The card represents sacrifice and the willingness to face short-term losses to ensure long-term gains. The Fool must learn patience and how to act strategically to achieve the result he wants. He may also benefit from a different perspective on the problem at hand. An immediate advantage must be given up, but will eventually be replaced by a much better opportunity. All expectations should be surrendered for the time being.

DEATH

KEYWORDS:

endings, loss, mourning,
acceptance, adjustment, change,
transition, rebirth, renewal

The card of Death depicts a skeleton with a scythe moving across a field of disembodied parts, most notably even the be-crowned head of a king. This suggests that the old order has ended and a new era is about to begin. At this stage in the journey, the Fool must accept approaching endings and uncertainty about the future. The endings may be difficult and painful, but we must learn to accept them. After a period of mourning and adjustment, we will be able to move on and embark on a new path. Change is inevitable. As we come to terms with this loss, we are transformed to enjoy a brighter future.

TEMPERANCE

THE DEVIL

KEYWORDS:
balanced temperament, harmony, moderation, cooperation, compromise, adaptability, relationship

KEYWORDS:
lust, greed, rage, primal instincts, secrets, the shadow, success in career and personal interests

The Temperance card shows the figure of an angel pouring liquid from one vessel into another. This indicates that feelings are able to flow freely. It may signify a guardian angel watching over us. The card represents balance, healing and harmony. The Fool has learnt to master his thoughts and feelings and can now have harmonious relationships with others. We should act in moderation; compromise is the key to any problem. We have the ability to manage a situation and resolve problems. Events will run smoothly and success can be achieved. This card indicates that good relationships are possible.

The Devil card may fill us with dread because the Devil is a Christian symbol of evil. The card asks us to confront the shadowy, instinctual part of ourselves. Following the perfect balance of the angel in the Temperance card, the Fool is reminded of those parts of himself that are self-serving and uncooperative, which he tries to keep hidden away, even from himself. When this card appears, that which we don't like to admit about our own character and desires may be trying to break into our consciousness. We may encounter these unwelcome qualities in others or in our dreams. A neglected part of us needs to be heard. Personal gain and success in one's career is indicated by this card. We are advised to act in our own interests.

THE TOWER

THE STAR

KEYWORDS:

conflict, overthrow, disruption, disapproval, sudden and unexpected change

KEYWORDS:

hope, faith, meaning, inspiration, promise, healing, protection, new horizons

The Tower card shows a tall building that has been struck by lightning. It is in flames and about to topple over. The lightning signifies that the gods are angry or disapproving. The Fool encounters sudden and disruptive changes and crises which force him to question his journey. This card suggests that the times are volatile, things are not going according to plan and the old order is in danger of being overthrown. We should not try to hold on and save the toppling tower; it is better to stand back and wait for things to settle. We may face uncertainty for a while. This card asks us to re-evaluate our current path. A sudden, complete change may be the best way forward.

The Star is a welcome symbol of hope, inspiration and rebirth to the Fool in the wake of the difficulties and uncertainties encountered in the Devil and Tower cards.

In this card we see a star shining brightly in the sky above a beautiful woman who is emptying jugs of water into a stream. It represents feelings being returned to their source. Healing is possible and our sense of well-being is renewed. There is hope for the future and new possibilities are beginning to form. We are ready to give and receive love. The Star promises change for the better. This is a good time to meet new people, apply for jobs and aspire towards what is really important to us.

THE MOON

KEYWORDS:
intuition, imagination, dreams, unconscious, fears, confusion, deception, disillusionment

The Moon is associated with night, the unconscious realm and the dream world, where our deepest fears and imaginations run wild. The Fool has encountered a period of confusion and disillusionment. Where is the promise of the previous card and what does the journey hold next? Situations are vague and unclear; matters are not what they seem. We can act without being seen! We are advised to avoid deception and paranoia. At this time we can more easily tap into our unconscious and find creative solutions to problems. The way ahead is foggy, but we should allow our intuition to guide us.

THE SUN

KEYWORDS:
joy, optimism, clarity, trust, courage, ambition, success, opportunity, health, vitality, happiness

The Sun, shown shining on twin boys, is symbolic of life in full bloom. The Fool has passed through his dark night and the way ahead is clear again. He knows where he is going and what he wants to achieve and he meets with success in all his endeavours. Indicating energy, joy, optimism and worldly success, this card suggests that it is the perfect moment to embrace opportunities and live life to the full. When this card appears in a spread, it promises good health, happiness and perhaps even the birth of a baby.

JUDGEMENT

THE WORLD

KEYWORDS:
reward for past effort,
re-evaluation, responsibility,
outcome, resolution, acceptance

KEYWORDS:
integration, fulfillment,
achievement, completion, ending,
final reward, success

The Judgement card shows an angel, possibly Gabriel, sounding a trumpet above figures rising from their graves. It echoes the Day of Judgement referred to in the Bible, when Christ and his angels will return to Earth and even the dead will be judged on their deeds. This card can be understood to bring us the reward in life that we deserve. The Fool is forced to look at where he has come from, how he has behaved and the choices he has made. It marks a point at which we must re-evaluate our lives. We may need to learn hard lessons and be held responsible for past actions. We are advised to come to a resolution and move on with a clean slate. The card can also refer to judgements in law.

The World, represented by a dancing woman, is the final card in one complete cycle. The creatures at each corner of this card signify the Christian tradition of the four missionaries – angel, eagle, lion and bull. These also represent the four elements and four suits of the tarot. The Fool has accomplished much and learnt what he is capable of along the way. Challenges have been faced and battles fought and won.

He is now ready to resume his position at the start of a new cycle. New challenges beckon and they can be approached with confidence.

All things will be possible for him in the fullness of time.

ACE OF WANDS

KEYWORDS:
beginning, change, opportunity, adventure, creativity, hope, action

The Ace of Wands signifies new beginnings and opportunities that can mark a change of direction in a person's life. There is the chance to embark on a journey or adventure, which may be sparked off by a new job opportunity, enterprise or relationship. The situation is full of hope and creative potential. It can also presage a birth in the family. Follow your intuition in taking up the right opportunities. Decide what you want to do and act quickly or you may miss your chance.

TWO OF WANDS

KEYWORDS:
rest after hard work, patience, trust, planning for the future

The Two of Wands indicates that a new goal or project is on the horizon. It has taken courage, care and determination to formulate your plan, so now you can stand back and allow it to unfold and grow. Leaving the matter alone to allow the magic to work can lead to a period of restlessness. Patience and trust in the future are required. At this time you should make plans for the next stage and work out what to do once your creative endeavours have taken root and started to grow. Negotiations with others may be required. Travel may be indicated for you.

THREE
OF WANDS

KEYWORDS:
accomplishment, success,
satisfaction, progression

The Three of Wands represents hopes
and plans that have been realized in the world.
Your ships are coming in and success is on
the horizon. The first stage of a project has
been completed and there is a feeling of great
satisfaction and pride in your accomplishment.
But remember there is much work ahead
so you must not become complacent. Avoid
arrogance and remember you have not always
been this fortunate and could lose your fortune
again. The momentum of your success may
propel you into the next stage of your project
or creative endeavour.

FOUR
OF WANDS

KEYWORDS:
reward, blessing, celebration,
happiness, harmony, romance

The Four of Wands suggests that you can
reap the rewards of your achievements. The
card promises a time of peace and harmony. It
is a temporary calm before the storm – more
hard work and energy will be required again
soon to resolve problems and conflicts that
will arise. But for the time being a great deal of
satisfaction and celebration is in order.

Be charming and amiable and enjoy sharing
your success with others. Romance may be in
the air.

FIVE OF WANDS

KEYWORDS:
fighting, conflict, obstacles,
compromise

The fives of each suit mark the crunch points along the journey. The Five of Wands suggests conflict, as demonstrated by the fight scene depicted on some card decks. It can also indicate the possibility of lawsuits. In your effort to accomplish your goals you have had to make difficult decisions and possibly cut corners or stepped on other people's toes along the way. This may have been unavoidable, but now you must battle it out. Try not to compete, but find a way to resolve the matter; compromise, if necessary. You need to hammer out the problem and find a resolution. If you behave honourably, things could turn out to your advantage.

SIX OF WANDS

KEYWORDS:
success, leadership, resolution,
fortune, acclaim

In the Six of Wands, problems have been dealt with and a matter is on the point of being successfully resolved. You have the support of friends and colleagues in realising your aims. Good news is on the way, so don't give up now. You should stay true to your original vision and goals. The card may indicate that you will receive public acclaim for your activities and efforts. Exams will have a positive outcome. Relationships are about to take a turn for the better.

SEVEN OF WANDS

KEYWORDS:
upper hand, position of advantage, challenge, force, reassessment

With the Seven of Wands you face another battle with others, but this time you have the upper hand. Remember to play fair, but maintain control over a situation and keep applying force. In the process you will learn to harness your competitive instincts to defend yourself and your creative endeavours. The challenges you face can also help you to reassess your plans and goals and modify your behaviour as required. This will make you stronger and more successful in the long run.

EIGHT OF WANDS

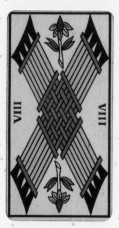

KEYWORDS:
movement, progress, back on track, goals on their way to being achieved

The Eight of Wands represents a plan on its way to completion. You are back on track after a period of conflict and delay. Obstacles have been cleared and the way is free. You are focused on attaining your goals and forging ahead with your plans. Things are on the move. News may herald major changes in your life. Events are moving quickly and circumstances will soon change for the better. Things you hoped for will come to pass. Travel may be required to secure a matter in your favour.

NINE OF WANDS

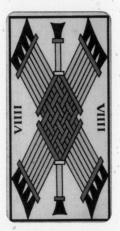

KEYWORDS:
final challenge, goal in
sight, perseverance, tenacity,
determination, courage to
overcome

The Nine of Wands represents last-minute challenges on your way to attaining a goal. You have come a long way and are determined not to give up now. Although it may not seem like it at the moment, what you have been hoping for is within reach. With your goal in sight, you find the courage and tenacity to give one final push. If you persevere, no obstacle can stand in your way for long. From deep within you must find the resources to keep going and remain hopeful. You have been given a final chance to prove you are worthy of success, it is up to you to rise to the challenge.

TEN OF WANDS

KEYWORDS:
achievement, attainment of goals,
satisfaction, experience gained,
rest and regeneration needed

In the Rider-Waite-Smith deck, the Ten of Wands shows an old man reaching his final destination. He is hunched over with the weight of his load. You have come a long way and are weighed down with the responsibility of turning your vision into reality. Your efforts are about to pay off, but at a cost for you have been shaped by bitter experience and have lost the innocence and optimism of youth. As you reach the end of the cycle you can find satisfaction in all your achievements so far. You will need to rest and recharge your batteries so that new ideas can form and you can start the process again.

PAGE OF WANDS

KEYWORDS:
active, playful, imaginative,
inspired, creative, youthful, folly

The Page of Wands is an active and boisterous youth with a fertile imagination. This card represents the urge to explore and play, to follow your dreams and look for new experiences and adventures. The Page seeks to avoid the responsibility that comes with maturity. When this card appears, it may represent a person, young or old, whose behaviour is eternally youthful. It may also represent your own need to break from stifling habits and responsibilities and develop these creative qualities within yourself.

KNIGHT OF WANDS

KEYWORDS:
honourable, courageous, hasty,
unreliable, aggressive, volatile,
new direction

The Knight of Wands is a great warrior who loves to take risks and prove himself worthy. An honourable opponent, he defends the vulnerable and fights for their cause. He can be hot-headed and temperamental and may rush to conclusions. The card may describe someone you know who fits these characteristics, or could indicate that you need to develop your warrior-like qualities to defend yourself or your loved ones. The Knight of Wands often signifies a move to a new home or a new direction in life.

QUEEN
OF WANDS

KEYWORDS:
strong, courageous, generous,
vibrant, creative, wise, intuitive

The Queen of Wands is a wise woman,
independent and authoritative, imaginative
and intuitive, strong and courageous. She
knows what she wants and how to get it.
The Queen makes a warm, lively host who
is generous with her gifts. The card may
describe a woman you know who fits these
characteristics, or may indicate that you need
to develop these qualities yourself.

KING
OF WANDS

KEYWORDS:
intuitive, decisive, active,
inspirational, visionary

The King of Wands is a mature man
of vision who inspires others. He has strong
leadership qualities and uses his wisdom and
powers of intuition to guide him in decision-
making. Sprightly and full of energy, the King
engages with life to the full. The card could
describe a man you know who fits these
characteristics or indicate that you need to
develop these qualities of leadership, activity
and inspiration in yourself.

ACE OF CUPS

KEYWORDS:
love, joy, happiness, abundance,
relationship, emotional expression,
fertility

The Ace of Cups, like the overflowing waters pictured on some card decks, indicates freely flowing emotions which need to find expression. There is potential for great emotional fulfilment. Deeply satisfying love and happiness are possible. The Ace of Cups represents the start of a new relationship or it can indicate a marriage proposal. There is the chance of a fresh start and a new lease of life. There is great hope for the future – your emotions will sustain you and love will find a way!

TWO OF CUPS

KEYWORDS:
new relationship, attraction,
romance, harmony, satisfaction,
conception, emotional fulfilment

The Two of Cups heralds the start of a new relationship, romantic attraction or connection with another person. You have the capacity for deep satisfaction and fulfilment. It feels as though you have met your match in another person. You see yourself reflected and mirrored back by your partner and find out about new aspects of your character through his or her eyes. Existing relationships are strengthened. The card can indicate a marriage union or conception of a child or perhaps another creative endeavour.

THREE OF CUPS

KEYWORDS:
pleasure, joy, marriage, birth, feasting, merriment, celebration, abundance, fortune

The Three of Cups indicates that there will be a happy gathering of people. This card may herald a pregnancy or marriage proposal or success in a creative endeavour close to your heart. You can be proud of your achievements. Joy and cause for celebration are indicated. This is a time to share your good fortune with others. You have renewed faith in the power of love.

FOUR OF CUPS

KEYWORDS:
dissatisfaction, boredom, discontent, depression, crisis, re-evaluation, self-questioning

For some reason you feel unhappy and discontented with your lot. You are in danger of developing a careless attitude towards life and becoming apathetic. You are entering a period of personal crisis and questioning and you have temporarily lost your connection with loved ones. You may feel that something is lost or missing from your life. The card indicates that you don't realise how fortunate you are. You need to take time to re-evaluate your life and decide what is really important to you.

FIVE OF CUPS

KEYWORDS:
loss, sorrow, regret, despair, betrayal, neglect, emotional breakdown, relationship breakup

The Five of Cups can presage a relationship or marriage breakup. The image on some decks shows a man in a black cloak turning his back and withdrawing from the world. Three cups have been spilled on the ground, indicating relationships that have been lost or thrown away. However, two full cups remain: this means you have a chance to hold on to whatever is left. You should think carefully before coming to a decision, for the effect could have consequences for yourself and your loved ones.

SIX OF CUPS

KEYWORDS:
calm, serenity, acceptance, simple pleasures, nostalgia, old friends, new hope and opportunity

The Six of Cups is the calm after an emotional storm. Although things might not be perfect, you learn to accept your limits and find a new appreciation of those close to you and with whom you share your life. Your thoughts may be focused on the past and you may start to idealise the 'good times' as you remember them. An old friend may re-enter your life and help you come to terms with what you have become, bringing a fresh opportunity and a new lease of life. New friendships can also blossom. Hope in the future will be renewed.

SEVEN OF CUPS

KEYWORDS:
decision, choice, dream, vision,
imagination, new path

The Seven of Cups suggests you are at a crossroads in life or in a particular matter. You have a very important decision to make and there appears to be more than one option open to you. Each cup in this card is filled with a different option. You may rely on the imagination, a dream or a vision to choose the right path. But you are advised to remain grounded and realistic when working with the imaginary realm or your decisions will be short-lived and you won't be able to stick with them for too long. Think before you choose.

EIGHT OF CUPS

KEYWORDS:
retreat, escape, abandonment,
loss, dissatisfaction, time out,
perspective needed

The Eight of Cups indicates that you may need to go away for a while to work out what is really important to you. You are unfulfilled and dissatisfied with your choices and find it difficult to choose something and stick with it. Nothing seems to bring the satisfaction for which you are yearning. You must find a way to gain some perspective on your life before deciding what to do next. You may need to find a way to let something go and trust that things are on the right track. You may also need to lose something for a while before it comes back.

NINE
OF CUPS

KEYWORDS:

wishes fulfilled, hopes realised,
positive outcome, childbirth, joy,
success, reward

The Nine of Cups is known as the 'nine
months card' and indicates the birth of a baby
or another creative endeavour. Something you
have tended and nurtured has come to fruition.
You are brimming with joy and the world is
filled with hope again. Health and happiness
are offered and the problems of the past have
evaporated. A wish will be fulfilled and things
will work out unexpectedly well. You can enjoy
your good fortune and find satisfaction in what
you have achieved.

TEN
OF CUPS

KEYWORDS:

lasting happiness, joy, fulfilment,
emotional stability, fortunate
outcome

The Ten of Cups is a card of emotional
security and long-lasting fortune in matters
of the heart. More happiness than you might
have thought possible will be yours. The card
indicates you have met, or will meet, the person
with whom you want to spend the rest of your
life. A situation has the best possible outcome.
A stable, lasting relationship and family life are
indicated. You can relax and enjoy the rewards
of your efforts and good fortune.

PAGE OF CUPS

VALET·DE·COUPE

KEYWORDS:
sensitive, sympathetic, kind,
imaginative, poetic, lazy,
daydreamer

The Page of Cups is a sensitive youth – a
kind, generous soul who is easily hurt, feels
other people's pain and is sympathetic to their
needs. The Page may be naturally lazy at times
and prone to daydreaming. He needs plenty
of space to play and explore the imaginative
realm. He or she may be oversensitive and may
not take criticism well. News from a loved one
could be indicated. This card may suggest a
character who displays these qualities, or infer
that these characteristics need to be developed
within ourselves.

KNIGHT OF CUPS

CAVALIER·DE·COUPE

KEYWORDS:
romantic, chivalrous, idealistic,
questing, highly principled, on a
mission

The Knight of Cups is the knight in
shining armour of the pack, in all his romantic
splendour. He rides around the kingdom
searching for his love, ready to save her from
any misfortune and ride off with her into the
sunset. The Knight may also be on another
quest – to seek the Holy Grail and restore the
health of the King, bringing balance, peace
and harmony to the kingdom. This card may
describe a chivalrous young man or woman
with a sense of mission and high ideals or
it may show these characteristics within
ourselves.

QUEEN OF CUPS

KEYWORDS:

emotional, sensitive, caring, peace-loving, harmonious, imaginative, creative talents

The Queen of Cups is in touch with her feelings. Wise and peace-loving, she is in tune with others. She is sensitive, sympathetic and kind-hearted. A good listener, she can advise others on matters that are causing concern. The Queen is a highly imaginative woman with creative gifts and talents. This card can represent a mature woman in your life with these characteristics or it can refer to these qualities in your own character.

KING OF CUPS

KEYWORDS:

kind, honourable, responsible, respected, considerate, easily swayed

The King of Cups is a kind, honourable male who is trusted and respected by others. He is naturally caring and puts the needs of his subjects first.

A just and fair ruler, he has earned the respect of others. He can be easily swayed and manipulated, however, so may become distrustful of others' motives. This card can be chosen to represent an individual with these qualities, or it may highlight these tendencies within ourselves.

ACE OF SWORDS

KEYWORDS:
beginning, hope, ideals, principles,
justice, conquest, new direction

The Ace of Swords stands for your
principles and ideals. You have decided to
embark on a new life or take a new direction
and have high expectations of your future.
Justice will be done. You do not wish to
compromise your strongly held beliefs. The
card may indicate the birth of a child, bringing
great hope for the future. You are asked to have
faith in yourself and your ability to overcome
any challenges that lie ahead.

TWO OF SWORDS

KEYWORDS:
tension, balance, stalemate,
difficult decision, action needed

The Two of Swords indicates that a matter
is in the balance and a difficult decision must
be made. You cannot decide between two
options open to you. There is a suggestion that
the way ahead is obscured. You must make a
decision and stick by it. You should act now
and not allow fears and doubts to hold you
back. The sooner you make a decision, the
sooner you can move on and find relief from a
situation that is hanging over you.

THREE OF SWORDS

KEYWORDS:
conflict, struggle, heartache, disappointment, arguments, tears, separation

The Three of Swords suggests the experience of pain and disappointment in matters of the heart, perhaps because of a love triangle. Feelings may be sacrificed in the interest of rational thinking. Quarrels and squabbles with loved ones are indicated. A separation of some kind may result. In gaining some distance from the matter you will find relief and realise that change was necessary in the long run.

FOUR OF SWORDS

KEYWORDS:
rest, retreat, withdrawal, recuperation, relief from anxieties, rebuilding strength

The Four of Swords offers solace from a matter that has caused anguish. Something has been lost and part of you feels as though it has died with it. You need time alone to contemplate what has happened and where things might have gone wrong. You must rebuild your strength and reorganise your thoughts before you are ready to face the world again.

FIVE OF SWORDS

KEYWORDS:
unfair play, dishonour,
belligerence, loss, facing
consequences

The Five of Swords indicates unfair play
and belligerent actions without consideration
of their effects in the long run. You may have
the upper hand in a matter, but your victory
is double-edged and causes as much sorrow
to you as it does to your adversaries. You have
acted dishonourably and disobeyed authority
to gain the upper hand. You must swallow your
pride and approach a situation honestly and
be prepared to face the consequences of your
actions.

SIX OF SWORDS

KEYWORDS:
solace, respite, retreat, healing,
journey, insight, reputation
restored

The Six of Swords may suggest that every
ounce of strength has been sapped from you
following a tough time, but the worst has now
passed. The card indicates that a journey might
be the best way to resolve a matter; this may
be a journey in the literal sense or a journey
of the mind. You are confronted with your
subconscious thoughts and, as a result, insights
may arise. You should allow things to sort
themselves out without intervening. A matter
that has been causing you great concern is on
its way to being resolved.

SEVEN OF SWORDS

KEYWORDS:
cunning, guile, deceit, tact,
diplomacy, flexibility,
compromise for the greater good

The Seven of Swords in some decks shows a figure stealing swords from a military camp. While such an act may be dishonourable and your personal principles may be compromised, your actions may be necessary for the greater good. This card suggests there are times when your beliefs and ideals must be flexible and you should adapt them to the task at hand. Life throws many situations at us and we can't afford to be too rigid in our thinking when we come to deal with them.

EIGHT OF SWORDS

KEYWORDS:
restriction, mistrust, inability to
act, indecision, imprisonment,
isolation from others

The Eight of Swords represents restriction and mistrust. A situation seems hopeless and you can't see a way out. You may feel trapped and hemmed in by your insistence on going it alone. You have run out of excuses and of ways to avoid making a decision – there is no escape. You must learn to trust others and should not be afraid to ask for help. You need to rebuild your connection with others and end your isolation before a decision is possible.

NINE
OF SWORDS

KEYWORDS:
fear, doubt, anxiety, nightmares,
troubled conscience, suffering,
despair

The Nine of Swords represents great anxiety and suffering. Your hopes have been dashed, you are filled with fear and doubt and you struggle to come to terms with a matter. You blame yourself for an unfortunate outcome, but need to keep things in perspective. While it is necessary to face your part in a situation, you are only human and will make mistakes. You need to forgive and accept your limitations before you can lay the past to rest and move on.

TEN
OF SWORDS

KEYWORDS:
endings, misfortune, loss, defeat,
new understanding, fresh
perspective

The Ten of Swords represents defeat and marks the end of a difficult matter. At the end of a long struggle, something has been irrevocably lost. Ultimately, the outcome is not one you wanted or welcomed. However, you must put the past behind you and move on to the next stage of the cycle. While you have been defeated on this occasion, lessons have been learned and you will move on with a new understanding of yourself and a fresh perspective.

PAGE OF SWORDS

KNIGHT OF SWORDS

KEYWORDS:
curiosity, intelligence, wit, honesty, independence, clash with authority

KEYWORDS:
fighter, warrior, reformer, prepared to make sacrifices for just causes

The Page of Swords is a clever, witty youth with a natural curiosity and inquisitive nature. He is in the process of developing his own ideas and beliefs and may frequently clash with authority over differences of opinion. The youth's independent ideas and curious spirit should be encouraged and nurtured rather than quashed. This card may represent a boy or girl who displays these qualities or may suggest that such gifts should be developed by the querent.

The Knight of Swords is a brave warrior who fights for the causes he believes in and is charged to protect. The Knight challenges injustice wherever he sees it and shows courage against all odds. He is willing to make sacrifices to uphold his principles and fights for justice, fairness and reform. Change will be brought about. This card may represent a young man or woman who displays these qualities or could suggest the time is right for the querent to personally develop such characteristics.

QUEEN OF SWORDS

REYNE · D'EPEE

KEYWORDS:
just, fair, intelligent, faithful, warrior, strong beliefs, idealistic, highly principled.

The Queen of Swords has a strong mind and keen intelligence. With a cool exterior, she may sometimes seem icy or aloof, but she is always kind and fair toward her subjects. The Queen will argue her opinions with a clear head and keen insight. She is not afraid to fight for her principles if her duties require it. When this card is selected, it may represent a female who displays these qualities or may indicate the time is right for these characteristics to be developed by the querent.

KING OF SWORDS

CAVALIER · D'EPEE

KEYWORDS:
intelligent, logical, fair, law-maker, judge, counsellor, warrior, strategist

The King of Swords is intelligent and known for his keen sense of logic and clear-headedness. He is an excellent judge and counsellor to his people and a capable warrior and military strategist. He has many innovative ideas, encourages reform and change and runs an orderly, civilised society. When this card is selected, it may represent a man who displays these qualities or could suggest that they should be developed by the querent.

ACE OF PENTACLES

KEYWORDS:

new venture, opportunity, promise of wealth, achievement

The Ace of Pentacles suggests a new opportunity or venture that will put our innate talents to good use. Like the other aces, this card represents high hopes for success and an opportunity to make something of our talents, provided we use them wisely. It also foretells the start of a prosperous time if it is drawn during a time of material shortages and financial hardship.

TWO OF PENTACLES

KEYWORDS:

balance, weighing up pros and cons, careful consideration, common sense, responsible decision-making

The Two of Pentacles is concerned with juggling two different duties, weighing up the pros and cons of a matter and making a carefully considered decision. In the image on the Rider-Waite-Smith deck, the figure balances two pentacles that are connected by the symbol of a cosmic lemiscate. This indicates that the figure must keep all his responsibilities in balance. You are challenged to make the most practical choice you can.

THREE
OF PENTACLES

KEYWORDS:
craftsperson, skilled artisan,
recognition of abilities,
achievement

The Three of Pentacles indicates that
you will be recognised for your skills and
achievements. Your handiwork is appreciated
by others. You have worked hard and earned
your success so far. While establishing a new
venture you have honed your skills and built
a good reputation. Now you must reassess
your goals and develop in a new direction You
can start another project from a position of
strength. Financial affairs will blossom.

FOUR
OF PENTACLES

KEYWORDS:
thrift, over-protectiveness, lack
of generosity, mistrust, paranoia,
isolation

The Four of Pentacles represents a
withholding, ungenerous nature. You are
afraid of losing what you have gained, so you
hold on tightly to everything. You begin to
become paranoid about other people's motives
and are so afraid of losing what you have
that you lose touch with others and become
unapproachable. This card can indicate
a tendency toward obsessive compulsive
behaviour, hypochondria and a fear of taking
risks. It warns that self-imposed isolation and
the desire for total control mean you are in
danger of pushing away those who love you.

FIVE OF PENTACLES

KEYWORDS:
financial worries, fear of loss,
destitution, failure, shame,
re-evaluation, starting again

The Five of Pentacles indicates financial worries and fear of loss or failure. It suggests both material and spiritual impoverishment. The card may presage the failure of a venture, loss of a job or redundancy. You feel you have not lived up to your high standards and expectations. Your fear of loss may have led to this situation. You must reassess your behaviour and regain faith in your talents and abilities. You have the capacity to work hard, rebuild your reputation and achieve your ambitions.

SIX OF PENTACLES

KEYWORDS:
success, sharing of wealth,
charity, philanthropy, giving
back to society

The Six of Pentacles signifies the sharing of good fortune with others. You have learned the lesson of the previous cards and now understand the consequence of holding on too tightly to material possessions. Plans are working out, you have succeeded in rebuilding your reputation in the world and can celebrate your success with others. Much satisfaction is gained from sharing time and money with worthy causes.

SEVEN OF PENTACLES

KEYWORDS:
rest after work, disappointing
returns, re-evaluation of projects,
redirecting efforts

The Seven of Pentacles indicates
weariness after a period of hard work and
suggests pausing to assess what you have
achieved so far. It asks you to re-evaluate your
plans and take stock of a situation. Are you
on the best route to success? Perhaps you are
overworked and disappointed with the rewards
of your labours. A period of recuperation and
regeneration may be necessary and you might
want to take a short break if you can afford it.
You should not lose faith, but implement the
improvements that are now needed.

EIGHT OF PENTACLES

KEYWORDS:
new skills, apprenticeship,
confidence, job satisfaction,
reward

The Eight of Pentacles represents learning
a new skill. You may be training in a new trade
fairly late in life. You are slowly but surely
gaining mastery in your work and can reap the
rewards of your efforts so far. Financial gain
and job satisfaction are indicated. Faith in your
skills and confidence that you will achieve your
ambitions will help you stay on the right path.

NINE OF PENTACLES

KEYWORDS:
pleasure, self-esteem, humility, realistic evaluation, sense of achievement, satisfaction, windfall

The Nine of Pentacles indicates that you can take pleasure and satisfaction in your work and reap the rewards of your labours. You have worked hard to develop your talents and abilities and have proved yourself a capable and worthy member of society. You are realistic about your limitations and recognise that you have had failures along the way. However, you can be proud of everything you have achieved so far and can draw great satisfaction from recognising your journey to success. An unexpected windfall is also indicated.

TEN OF PENTACLES

KEYWORDS:
security, inheritance, lasting success, satisfaction, sharing, rewards, contentment

Ten of Pentacles indicates that lasting success and material satisfaction have been achieved. You have earned the right to relax and enjoy what has been accumulated through your efforts. The card suggests that you have also gained an inner sense of security. In addition to your personal wealth, a family inheritance may ensure that you live in comfort for a long time. Enjoying the company of your family and loved ones and sharing your material fortune with them brings the greatest pleasure now. The card indicates a satisfying home life.

PAGE
OF PENTACLES

KEYWORDS:
diligent, reliable, mature, loyal,
steady, hardworking, responsible

The Page of Pentacles is mature beyond
his years and is the type of youth you can
depend on – reliable and hard working in his
studies and keen to start working from an
early age. The Page of Pentacles makes a loyal,
steady friend. A message about money may be
received. The Page may represent a youthful
person who displays these qualities, or may
highlight the need to nurture these qualities
in ourselves.

KNIGHT
OF PENTACLES

KEYWORDS:
sensible, considerate, stable,
responsible, respectful, practical,
nervous

The Knight of Pentacles is a practical,
sensible, considerate character, with a strong
sense of duty and respect for others. Unlike
the other knights, the Knight of Pentacles acts
with caution, taking care not to rock the boat.
Knights are normally very active principals
who fight for change of some sort. This
knight needs to find a way of balancing these
two tendencies or they will pull in different
directions and lead to nervous tension. This
card may represent a young man or woman
known for these qualities, or may indicate the
need to develop them in our own characters.

QUEEN OF PENTACLES

KING OF PENTACLES

KEYWORDS:
generous stable, sensible, down-to-earth, warm, comforting, healthy, contented

KEYWORDS:
sensible, fair, honest, patient, generous, practical, traditional, stable, humble, self-reliant

The Queen of Pentacles is practical, down-to-earth and generous with her gifts. She has an affinity with nature and animals and radiates comfort and confidence in her body. She enjoys tending to her surroundings and taking care of others. She can be relied upon to give fair, sensible advice and find practical solutions to problems. This card may represent a mature woman who displays these qualities, or can highlight the need to develop them in ourselves.

The King of Pentacles is an honest, generous leader who has worked hard and achieved great success. He upholds his duties and traditions and respects his ancestral heritage. The King finds practical solutions to problems and dislikes experimenting with new methods and technologies, preferring the old way of doing things. The King is kind, but has high expectations of others and expects them to have the same self-discipline and work ethic that he has. He is humble and self-reliant. This card can represent a mature man who displays these qualities, or can indicate the need to recognise them in ourselves.

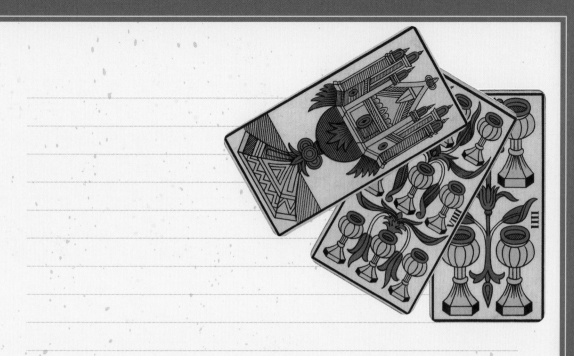